WORLD WAR II
TRIVIA QUIZ BOOK

Volume 1:
Europe & North Africa

**Forgotten facts about
this century's biggest land grab**

by Erhard Konerding

THE SOUTHFARM PRESS, Middletown, CT

THE SOUTHFARM PRESS
A division of
Haan Graphic Publishing Services, Ltd.
P.O. Box 1296
Middletown, CT 06457

ISBN: 0 913337 04 8

Second Printing: August, 1985

Printed in the United States of America

Composition by Typegraphics,
Marlborough, Connecticut

Cover photo of M7 "Priest" courtesy
of the U.S. Department of Defense.

CONTENTS

Chapter 1: Weapons   7

Chapter 2: People   17

Chapter 3: Air Power   27

Chapter 4: Naval Power   37

Chapter 5: Commandos and Resistance   45

Chapter 6: Acronyms   51

Chapter 7: D-Day   55

Chapter 8: Slang   62

Chapter 9: Chow Line   64

Chapter 10: Landmines—Questions to "blow your mind"   67

Further Reading   77

Answers are located at the end of each chapter.

"Not in vain" may be the pride of
those who survived and the epitaph
of those who fell.

Winston Churchill

Weapons

Every bullet has its billet.

Prince William III of Orange

An incredible number of weapons were used in World War II, from commonly known tools of war such as the M-1 rifle, the German "88" artillery piece, the Spitfire fighter, and Sherman and Tiger tanks, to the many weapons and devices which were kept so secret that they are still not widely publicized. Even the weapons held by soldiers and sailors on many fronts have some obscure or surprising characteristics.

1. The portable Bailey Bridge, consisting of prefabricated steel girder sections, was named for its inventor, a (an):

A. Royal Canadian Navy officer
B. American professor from MIT
C. Australian engineer officer
D. British engineer

2. Ferdinand Porsche, best known for his postwar sports car designs, also created all but which of the following:

A. The amphibious military Volkswagen, Schwimmwagen (Typ 128)
B. The tank-destroyer "Elephant"
C. The Pzkfw V "Panther" tank
D. The original design for the "King Tiger" tank
E. The "Maus," (mouse), a 200-ton tank design

3. Only one Allied jet fighter saw operational combat service in World War II. It was the:

A. deHavilland Vampire F. Mk I
B. Bell P-59 Airacomet
C. Gloster Meteor F Mk III
D. Lockheed P-80 Shooting Star

4. Which of these standard army rifles has the largest caliber:

A. Enfield Mk. I (British)
B. Mauser Kar. 98k (German)
C. Garand M-1 (U.S.)
D. Mannlicher-Carcano (Italian)
E. Tokarev (USSR)

5. Which of these artillery pieces has the smallest caliber:

A. German 12 cm howitzer
B. British 25-pounder
C. U.S. M-1 105mm. howitzer
D. Soviet 100mm. antitank gun

6. More V-2 rockets were launched against this target than any other:

A. Brussels
B. London
C. Portsmouth
D. Antwerp

7. Hedgehog was the name for:

A. A German beach defense device of welded steel
B. An American concrete-busting armor-piercing shell
C. A British antisubmarine rocket system
D. A British tank trap devised by the Home Guard
E. A and C above
F. B and D above

8. The brilliant British inventor Barnes Wallis designed all but one of the following. Which was it?

A. The "Grand Slam" and "Tallboy" giant bombs
B. The geodesic Wellington bomber
C. The Dambuster bomb
D. The Mosquito plywood bomber
E. The R100 dirigible

Match the following secret weapons or devices with their functions:

9. ___ Window   A. A proximity fuse, which exploded near the
10. ___ Oboe   target
11. ___ Rebecca   B. An airborne radar jamming device
12. ___ Piperack   C. Strips of tinfoil to jam radars
13. ___ VT   D. Direction finding device used in conjunction
                           with the S-phone
                    E. Range and direction-finding instrument
                       system used by RAF bombers

14. German tanks used a distinctive numbering system. It consisted of:

A. One number superimposed above 3, all in a triangle; the top number was the individual tank number, the bottom 3 indicated the regiment, company, and platoon
B. Three numbers in red or white, or outlined in white or black; first number indicated company and battalion, second the platoon, third the individual vehicle
C. A chevron on the vehicle side: facing forward, backward, up or down to indicate company; stripes on the barrel to show platoon; and letters on the turret for individual vehicles

15. The bomb which nearly killed Hitler on July 20, 1944, was:

A. A modified Luftwaffe anti-personnel bomb
B. A British plastic bomb captured from SOE agents in France
C. A Wehrmacht land mine
D. A Russian sabotage device captured from Soviet partisans

16. The DeLisle Silent Commando Carbine Mk I consisted of:

A. An M-1 carbine with silencer and folding stock
B. A Sten Mk IV with silencer
C. A Lee-Enfield stock and action modified to fire .45 cal. rounds from a Colt pistol magazine, with silencer
D. A Mauser M-1896 9mm. pistol with shoulder stock and silencer

17. The "stuffed rat" was:

A. A typical meal for Russian prisoners in Germany
B. Rat skin containing explosive, planted by SOE saboteurs in coal bins, meant to explode in boilers
C. Nickname for a camouflage suit worn by snipers in Britain's Home Guard
D. The insulting name given to Hermann Goering by the Soviet editorial cartoonists

Wehrmacht armored vehicles were often named after animals, a practice continued by today's West German Bundeswehr. Can you identify each of the following German WWII armored fighting vehicles:

18. ___ Hetzer (harrier)
19. ___ Guderian Ente (Guderian duck)
20. ___ Moebelwagen (furniture truck)
21. ___ Brummbaer (grizzly bear)
22. ___ Nashorn (rhino)
23. ___ Hummel (bumblebee)

A. Quad 20mm. AA guns on Panzer IV chassis
B. 75mm. antitank gun on Czech T38 tank chassis
C. 75mm. antitank gun on Panzer IV chassis
D. 150mm. howitzer on Panzer IV chassis
E. 88mm. antitank gun on Panzer IV chassis
F. 120mm. howitzer on Panzer IV chassis

24. The Sturmgeschuetz, a German antitank vehicle with a heavy gun mounted in a fixed armored superstructure rather than a revolving turret, was the idea of:

A. General Heinz Guderian
B. Field Marshal Erich von Manstein
C. Field Marshal Hermann Goering
D. Adolf Hitler

25. *Rasputitsa* is the Russian name for:

A. The "scorched earth" policy
B. The rainy, muddy season of Autumn
C. The machine gun
D. The marshy area south of Leningrad

26. The Soviets used dogs laden with explosives to destroy German tanks. These dogs:

A. Were successful, but the need for dogs to carry messages and first aid supplies was more urgent
B. Were shot by the Germans before they could near the Panzers
C. Tried to crawl under the familiar-smelling Russian tanks they were trained with
D. Were eaten by the underfed Russian troops they were sent out among
E. B and C above

27. The crude and cheap, yet effective, 9mm. submachine Sten gun used widely by British forces, was named for:

A. Its designers, Messrs. Stephenson and Enderby
B. Its designers, Shepperd and Turpin, and the Royal Small Arms Factory at Enfield
C. Its typical stentorian noise
D. The Belgian cities of Steenkirk and Enville, where the design originated

28. The fast tank designs of J. Walter Christie, brilliant yet mercurial American inventor, greatly influenced the design of the:

A. British cruiser tank series
B. Soviet BT tanks and the T-34
C. The German Panzer IV and its variants
D. The M4 Sherman tank
E. A and B above
F. C and D above

29. The Malcolm hood and Galland hood (also called ERLA Haube) were, respectively, British and German solutions to a similar problem. These hoods were:

A. Attached to winter uniforms in Arctic areas to greatly add to their warmth and comfort
B. Improved tank gun mounts to improve ballistic protection and eliminate "shot traps"
C. Newer engine covers for trucks to improve ventilation and rain water runoff
D. Curved, streamlined cockpit canopies which improved pilot all-around vision

30. Of the 22 million jerry cans (5-gallon cans) furnished to the Allied armies in France from June to August, 1944, how many were lost, stolen, or destroyed by the end of August:

A. One-tenth
B. One-fifth
C. One-third
D. One-half

31. The Fairbairn-Sykes commando knife widely used by Royal Commandos, which was manufactured by Wilkinson and other British cutlers, was designed by:

A. Two British surgeons, who advised commandos on the most lethal use of the knife
B. Two British colonial officials who had studied Chinese martial arts
C. An Oxford professor of anatomy and one of his prize pupils
D. Two cutlery experts at the Wilkinson factory

32. The "combat box" was:

A. A portable pillbox, made out of concrete and steel
B. A staggered, tight flight formation of B-17's
C. The wooden container in which C-rations were packed
D. A parachute container dropped to OSS agents in France

33. German anti-aircraft and anti-tank gunners kept track of their score of "kills" by:

A. Marking silhouettes of the destroyed tank or airplane on the gun shield
B. Carving notches in the tires
C. Painting stripes on the gun barrel
D. Hanging streamers from the gun shield

34. The expression "50-mission crush" used in the Army Air Forces referred to:

A. A psychological syndrome, similar to "battle fatigue" suffered by pilots and other aircrew
B. The appearance of the typically wrinkled AAF uniform
C. A style of mashing one's hat to look as if it had been through many combat missions
D. The hug that crew members ritually gave one another after surviving 50 missions

35. The Chrysler multibank engine was:

A. A multiple-row radial aircraft engine experimentally installed in the prototype B-19 bomber
B. An enormously powerful engine intended for the Dodge 10-ton transporter truck
C. A turbine engine used in several classes of landing craft
D. 5 automobile engines on a common crankshaft, mounted in many Sherman tanks

36. The M1 "steel pot" helmet standardized for U.S. Army use in 1941:

A. Used the crown design of the British-style M1917 helmet, with the rim removed and side and rear pieces added
B. Consisted of two parts: the 2.3 lb. steel shell and the separate 11 oz. liner with strap and suspension
C. Was designed with the help of the Metropolitan Museum of Art in New York City
D. Was redesigned in 1943 with a special release on the strap which separated when pressure on the strap was so great as to cause injury to the wearer
E. All of the above
F. A and B only

37. The plywood deHavilland Mosquito bomber used by the RAF and Commonwealth air forces was:

A. Used in low-level daylight precision attacks on selected targets
B. Capable of carrying 4,000 lbs. of bombs from England to Berlin and returning
C. Used as a pathfinder aircraft, and in "spoofing" attacks on bombing raids
D. Also employed as fighter-bomber, night fighter, and anti-shipping aircraft
E. All of the above

38. These Navy men are:

A. Trying out a one-man amphibious landing craft, which was never put into service

B. Examining a captured German remote-control explosive vehicle, which was intended to help foil Allied landings

C. Testing the scale model for the proposed armored landing craft, the "Alligator"

D. Checking out the British "Beach Clearance Vehicle, Remote Control," used to explode breaches in beach obstacles

Weapons Answer Key

1. D	9. C	17. B	25. B	33. C
2. C	10. E	18. B	26. E	34. C
3. C	11. D	19. C	27. B	35. D
4. B	12. B	20. A	28. E	36. E
5. B	13. A	21. D	29. D	37. E
6. D	14. B	22. E	30. D	38. B
7. E	15. B	23. F	31. B	
8. D	16. C	24. B	32. B	

People

Death and sorrow will be the companions
of our journey; hardship our garment;
constancy and valor our only shield.
We must be united, we must be
undaunted, we must be inflexible.

Winston Churchill

1. Noel Coward, assisted by David Lean, directed the classic 1942 movie *In Which We Serve*. In the movie, Coward himself portrayed a fictionalized:

A. Captain Lord Louis Mountbatten and his ship, HMS Kelly
B. Admiral Henry Harwood and the HMS Exeter
C. Admiral Sir James Somerville and HMS Illustrious
D. Admiral Sir Andrew Cunningham, commander of the British fleet in the Mediterranean

Hollywood actors, both prewar and postwar, joined the armed forces in various capacities. Match the following silver screen stars or directors with their wartime careers:

2. ___ James Stewart
3. ___ Ronald Reagan
4. ___ Sterling Hayden
5. ___ Clark Gable
6. ___ John Huston
7. ___ Frank Capra

A. Air gunner on a B-17, saw combat tour over Europe
B. OSS officer in Italy and Yugoslavia
C. Filmed *Why We Fight* for the Army
D. AAF officer, never left USA
E. Bomber pilot over Europe
F. Made films for the Army, including *Battle for San Pietro* and *Report from the Aleutians*

British film stars and directors participated, too. Match:

8. ___ Leslie Howard
9. ___ Anthony Quayle
10. ___ Noel Coward
11. ___ Alfred Hitchcock
12. ___ David Niven

A. British intelligence officer on Gibraltar
B. Did counterintelligence work in South America
C. Directed 2 French-language films for Ministry of Information
D. Commando officer in Normandy and Germany, highly decorated
E. Lost when BOAC airliner was shot down by German fighters off France

13. William Wyler's Academy Award-winning 1942 film, *Mrs. Miniver,* starred Greer Garson in the title role of an Englishwoman during the Battle of Britain. Her husband was played by:

A. Walter Huston
B. Walter Pidgeon
C. Walter Brennan
D. Walter Slezak

14. Field Marshal Sir Bernard Law Montgomery often wore an Australian army bush hat adorned with the cap badges of the many regiments under his command. When he wore his beret, it had only two cap badges. These were:

A. Special Air Service and Scots Guards
B. Wessex Regiment and his Field Marshal's rank badge
C. Royal Tank Regiment and his Field Marshal's rank badge
D. Royal Army Ordnance Corps and 17/21 Lancers

15. Reinhard Heydrich, assassinated in Prague by 2 Czech patriots parachuted into Czechoslovakia by the British, was:

A. Chief of the Reichsicherheitshauptamt (RSHA)
B. "Protector" of Bohemia-Moravia
C. A Luftwaffe reserve fighter pilot
D. One of the architects of the "Final solution" to the "Jewish problem"
E. All of the above
F. B and D above only

16. Which of the following projects was the SS commando Otto Skorzeny *not* involved in:

A. Anti-resistance activities in Denmark
B. Infiltrating English-speaking German soldiers in U.S. uniforms behind American lines during the Battle of the Bulge
C. The canceled Operation Suicide, which proposed kamikaze flights in piloted V-1's
D. The "rescue" of Mussolini and his delivery to Germany
E. A failed attempt to assassinate the entire Red Army headquarters staff behind Russian lines
F. Rounding up conspirators in the failed Hitler assassination plot

17. Colonel Claus von Stauffenberg, who planted the bomb which nearly killed Hitler on July 20, 1944, had trouble placing the bomb properly, partly because of serious wounds he had suffered in North Africa. He had lost:

A. One eye
B. Most of his right arm
C. Three fingers of his left hand
D. His right leg below the knee, and his left foot
E. All of the above
F. A, B, and C
G. A, C, and D

18. Vladimir Peniakoff was:

A. A Russian field marshal executed by Stalin after failing to recapture the Crimean peninsula
B. Leader of "Popski's Private Army," a British LRDG group which harassed German forces in Africa and Italy
C. The highest-ranking Polish officer executed in the Katyn forest
D. A Soviet spy in Switzerland, member of the "Red Orchestra"
E. Captured Soviet general who led Russian forces fighting for the Nazi's

19. The last action in the European theater for which a Congressional Medal of Honor was awarded (to Raymond Knight) was:

A. An air mission over Italy
B. A ground action in Germany
C. An armored battle in Czechoslovakia
D. An infantry attack in Austria

20. Sir Frederick Arthur Browning, founder and leader of the British parachute forces, was married to the well-known writer:

A. Agatha Christie
B. Virginia Woolf
C. Beatrix Potter
D. Daphne du Maurier

21. General Omar Bradley was originally called "The Soldier's General" by:

A. Dwight Eisenhower
B. Field Marshal Montgomery
C. The correspondent Ernie Pyle
D. The cartoonist Bill Mauldin

The great number of air battles over Western Europe, Russia, Italy, and Africa produced many air aces (an ace has shot down more than 5 enemy planes). The top aces defeated many opponents, sometimes on more than one front. Polish, Czech, French, and other aces from captive countries scored some of their victories in RAF service. Match these leading aces with their number of "kills":

22. ___ Group Captain C.R. Caldwell (Australian)   A. 32 kills
23. ___ Wing Cmdr. Witold Urbanowicz (Polish-RAF)   B. 33
24. ___ S/Ldr M.T. Pattle (South Africa)   C. 352
25. ___ Sgt. Josef Frantisek (Czech-Polish RAF)   D. 31⅓
26. ___ Flight Lt. George Beurling (Canada)   E. 41
27. ___ Major Erich Hartmann (German)   F. 28½
28. ___ Group Capt. J.E. Johnson (RAF)   G. 38
29. ___ W/Cdr. B. "Paddy" Finucane (Irish)   H. 20
30. ___ W/Cdr. C.F. Gray (New Zealand)   I. 31
31. ___ Col. Francis Gabreski (USAAF)   J. 27½
32. ___ S/Ldr P.H. Clostermann (France)   K. 28
33. ___ Ivan Kozhedub (USSR)   L. 62
34. ___ Flt. Mstr. Eino Juutilainen (Finland)   M. 94

The sons of both President Franklin Roosevelt and former President Theodore Roosevelt fought in World War II, in Europe and the Pacific. Match FDR's sons with their service careers:

35. ___ Elliot
36. ___ FDR, Jr.
37. ___ James
38. ___ John

A. USMC officer in Pacific
B. Navy ensign in Pacific
C. Naval officer at Operation Torch, later in Pacific
D. AAF general, though never pilot rated

Match TR's sons with their service careers:

39. ___ Archibald   A. Won Medal of Honor for Normandy action
40. ___ Kermit   B. Fought in the Pacific
41. ___ TR, Jr.   C. OSS member, and major in both U.S. and
                                   British armies

42. Popular American bandleader Glenn Miller disappeared while flying aboard a USAAF aircraft. What type of aircraft?

A. A Douglas C-47 Skytrain
B. A Beech C-45 Kansan
C. A Convair C-87 Liberator transport
D. A Noorduyn C-64 Norseman

43. Moshe Dayan, later to be Israel's Defense Minister, was known for his black eyepatch. He had lost his eye:

A. During the invasion of Syria in 1941, while scouting for the British
B. In an accident while training as an RAF pilot in Southern Rhodesia in 1944
C. While fighting as a member of the Jewish Legion in Italy
D. While teaching British paratroopers at Middle East Parachute School at Ramat David airfield in Palestine

44. Antoine de St.-Exupery, author of the best-selling children's book *The Little Prince,* was, during World War II:

A. An officer of the French Foreign Legion in Africa and Italy
B. A leader of the Maquis in the Lyon area until captured by the Gestapo in 1943
C. A pilot in the French, and later Free French Air Force; lost on a combat mission
D. One of Charles de Gaulle's most trusted aides from 1941 on

45. Pierre Koenig, Charles de Gaulle's Foreign Minister in the 1950's, participated in World War II as:

A. French Foreign Legion officer in Norway in 1940
B. Foreign Legion officer in France
C. Free French general in North Africa, decorated for action at Bir Hakeim
D. A leader of the French underground
E. All of the above

46. The British scientist who assessed the bombing campaign on Pantelleria and then suggested the "interdiction plan" to destroy German transport behind the Normandy front, was:

A. Ronald Lewin
B. Solly Zuckerman
C. George Lindeman
D. Henry Tizard

47. Hans Ulrich Rudel received the Knight's Cross with Gold Oak Leaves, one of Nazi Germany's highest awards. He was a:

A. Tank commander on the Eastern Front with more than 200 enemy tanks to his credit
B. Stuka pilot who destroyed more than 500 Russian tanks, and several Russian warships
C. Paratroop leader who distinguished himself in Holland, Norway, and Crete
D. U-Boat captain who sank more Allied shipping than any other

48. The American newsman who scooped all his colleagues by several hours with the story of the French surrender to the Germans at Compiegne was:

A. Edward R. Murrow
B. Walter Cronkite
C. William L. Shirer
D. Harry Reasoner

49. Wing Commander Douglas Bader, RAF, was unique among British World War II aces because he:

A. Had also been an ace in the first World War
B. Had only one eye
C. Had lost both legs
D. Needed eyeglasses to see clearly

50. Four Army lieutenants received posthumous Distinguished Service Crosses, and a unique Special Medal for Heroism granted by the President and Congress in 1961, for an action that took place on the S.S. Dorchester on February 3, 1943. These men, Lts. Clark Poling, George Fox, John Washington, and Alexander Goode:

A. Replaced the dead Navy gun crew, then successfully fought off an attacking German raider, but were killed by gunfire from the German ship
B. Were the Catholic, Protestant, and Jewish chaplains who gave up their life belts to other men as the Dorchester sank
C. Rescued the engine room crew from the flaming interior of the ship, but died from smoke inhalation later
D. Organized efforts to throw the blazing cargo of volatile materials overboard, but were killed in an explosion

51. Conscientious objectors, who refused to become combat troops because killing others violated their religious beliefs, were imprisoned in World War I. In World War II, American C.O.'s:

A. Became chaplains' assistants
B. Joined the armed forces as medics or corpsmen
C. Were subjects of dietary and psychological experiments
D. Worked for forestry and soil reclamation agencies, even becoming "smoke jumpers"
E. A and B above
F. B, C, and D only

52. American servicemen stationed in England, Wales, Scotland, and Northern Ireland, often married local women. How many GI war brides came from the British Isles?

A. 30,000

B. 70,000

C. 110,000

D. 150,000

U.S. Department of Defense

53. This fighting man, photographed in Italy, is:

A. A Russian "Cossack" in German service

B. A member of the Italian "Foreign Legion"

C. An Indian Army "sepoy"

D. A French North African "goumier"

People Answer Key

1. A	12. D	23. H	34. M	45. E
2. E	13. B	24. E	35. D	46. B
3. D	14. C	25. K	36. C	47. B
4. B	15. E	26. D	37. A	48. C
5. A	16. E	27. C	38. B	49. C
6. F	17. F	28. G	39. B	50. B
7. C	18. B	29. A	40. C	51. F
8. E	19. A	30. J	41. A	52. B
9. A	20. D	31. I	42. D	53. D
10. B	21. C	32. B	43. A	
11. C	22. F	33. L	44. C	

Air Power

Keep 'em flying.

Slogan of the Air Forces,
poster caption, World War II

The use of air power in the second World War was on a far more massive scale than ever seen before. Both tactical and strategic air power appeared on most war fronts. Air superiority was the key to victory, from the Nazi blitzkrieg to ultimate Allied victory in the West.

1. Unarmed Luftwaffe He59 floatplanes painted white and marked with red crosses were used to rescue pilots downed in the English Channel. The RAF:

A. Gave these aircraft a wide berth, and made no attempts to harass them
B. Attacked them with its rescue vessels, in order to get to the downed pilots first
C. Shot them down after the "Red Cross" planes were seen suspiciously close to British convoys
D. Allowed these planes to overfly British soil to rescue German pilots who parachuted down in coastal England

2. The Regia Aeronautica, or Italian Air Force, participated in the Battle of Britain by:

A. Sending observers along on most German missions over Britain between December 1940 and March 1941
B. Providing antiaircraft gun crews for German bomber bases in Belgium and France
C. Furnishing fighter cover over Luftwaffe bases to protect returning bombers from British intruder aircraft
D. Sending 80 bombers and 98 fighters which attacked England from October to December 1941

3. The German bombing of Rotterdam while negotiations for surrender were going on caused great physical damage and:

A. 12 deaths
B. 800-900 deaths
C. 2,300 deaths
D. 10,500 deaths (estimated)

4. In the German conquest of The Netherlands, the Luftwaffe lost:

A. 2 aircraft, both to accidents
B. 42 aircraft, 18 to German flak
C. 75 aircraft
D. Over 525 aircraft

The many hundreds of British airmen who fought in the Battle of Britain were aided by other Allied pilots. For example, there were 23 each from South Africa and Australia, 7 Americans, 14 Free French, 11 Irish, one each from Palestine, Jamaica, and Southern Rhodesia. Match these Allied countries with the number of airmen who participated in the battle.

		Took Part
5. ___ Czechoslovakia		A. 104
6. ___ New Zealand		B. 94
7. ___ Belgium		C. 154
8. ___ Poland		D. 27
9. ___ Canada		E. 93

10. The Finnish Air Force, between 1939 and 1945, used aircraft produced in:

A. Britain, France, and Germany
B. Sweden, Finland, and The Netherlands
C. Italy, the U.S., and U.S.S.R.
D. All of the above
E. B and C only

11. The first air raid of the war comprising more than 1,000 bombers was:

A. The German raid on Coventry
B. The RAF attack on Cologne on May 30, 1942
C. The RAF and USAAF destruction of Dresden in 1945
D. The USAAF attack on Schweinfurt

12. The German special operations group KG200 participated in:

A. The Mistletoe (Mistel) piggyback aircraft project
B. Remote-controlled bomb tests
C. Secret flights using captured RAF and USAAF aircraft
D. Deep-penetration flights over Allied territory
E. All of the above
F. A, B, and C only

13. German air convoys of giant Me323's to and from Africa in waning days of the Afrika Korps:

A. Were a tremendous success, and served as an example for the later use of such convoys in Russia
B. Were savagely attacked and nearly wiped out by RAF, USAAF, and South African aircraft
C. Lost their way and had to return to Sicily more often than not
D. Were cannibalized as shelter and firewood by the Wehrmacht

14. The famous "shark mouth" insignia painted boldly on Flying Tigers aircraft in China were inspired directly by the design's previous use on their own P-40's by:

A. No. 14 Squadron, RCAF
B. No. 2 OTU, SAAF
C. No. 112 Squadron, RAF
D. The French Normandie-Niemen Regiment in Russia

1942 was a year of great aircraft production, though the number of aircraft produced continued to increase. Which nations produced which number of airplanes in 1942:

15. ___ Soviet Union   A. 23,670
16. ___ Germany   B. 40,000
17. ___ United States   C. 15,550
18. ___ Great Britain   D. 48,000

19. When, on May 23, 1944, Adolf Hitler ordered the Me-262 to be built as a bomber only, which of his subordinates said: "Any small child could see that this is no bomber but a fighter!"

A. Hermann Goering
B. Adolf Galland
C. Willy Messerschmitt
D. Erhard Milch

20. The Me-321 *Gigant* glider was converted to a powered air transport by the addition of:

A. 8 BMW VI engines with constant-speed propellers
B. 4 Junkers Jumo 211 engines
C. 6 Hispano-Suiza engines built in France
D. 6 Gnome-et-Rhone engines removed from French bombers

21. The prototypes of both the Me109 and Ju87 Stuka first flew with the same engine. This powerplant was:

A. The Rolls-Royce Kestrel
B. The Pratt & Whitney Wasp
C. The Junkers Jumo 210
D. The Daimler-Benz DB601

22. The armored ground attack airplane *Il-2 Shturmovik* was the most widely produced Soviet warplane. The USSR produced:

A. 15,000
B. 27,000
C. 36,000
D. 45,000

23. The Luftwaffe expression *"Flak nach vorn!"* (Flak up front) means:

A. Look out for the anti-aircraft fire in front of you!
B. Move the anti-aircraft guns up front!
C. Those guys in front are really catching a lot of flak!
D. Roughly, the equivalent of: "Damn the torpedoes! Full speed ahead!"

24. On March 31, 1944, 96 RAF bombers were downed on a raid over Nuremberg. This was remarkable because:

A. "Bomber" Harris doesn't mention it in his memoirs
B. This was even less than the expected losses
C. The city is not shown on historical maps of RAF wartime raids
D. The Luftwaffe used Me-262 jets as night fighters for the first time in this raid
E. A and C above
F. A and D above

25. The USAAF raid on oil refineries in the Rumanian city of Ploesti on August 1, 1943, is well-known and documented. The AAF also bombed Ploesti:

A. On June 11-12, 1942
B. On January 22, 1943
C. In April, May, and June, 1944
D. On December 11, 1944
E. A and C above
F. B and D above

The USAAF considered the Ruhr Valley the best-defended target in the Reich. The next two on the list were:

26. ___ 2nd place   A. Berlin
27. ___ 3rd place   B. Budapest, Hungary
                      C. Vienna, Austria
                      D. Ploesti, Rumania
                      E. Pilsen, Czechoslovakia

28. The 15th Air Force, based in Foggia, Italy, had a song which went as follows:

> "It's still the same old story,
> The Eighth gets all the glory,
> While we go out and die . . .
> The fundamental things apply,
> As flak goes by."

This song parodied:

A. As Tears Go By
B. The Years Go By
C. As Time Goes By
D. Bye, Bye, Blackbird

Pilots who scored victories over foes often decorated their own craft with "kill marks" to signify number of victories. Which air forces used which system:

29. ___ Luftwaffe   A. Miniature national insignia of downed air-
30. ___ RAF &   craft
       USAAF   B. Frontal silhouette of downed aircraft type,
31. ___ Soviet Air   later vertical bars, one pilot even using labels
       Force   peeled from beer bottles!
32. ___ Finnish Air   C. Miniature national insignia of *own* air force
       Force   D. Small vertical bar, often with miniature
                          national insignia of downed aircraft

33. Me109G-5 and later marks of that fighter aircraft were known as *Beule* ("bulge") to their pilots because of:

A. The awkward underwing gondolas containing MG 151 20mm. cannon, which hampered performance
B. The cowling bulge which covered the breech of the 13mm. MG 131 machine gun
C. The bulge in the top of the wing to accommodate the larger landing wheel added to those aircraft
D. The bulky under-fuselage mount for bombs or fuel tanks
E. The way the pilots bulged out of the too-snug seat

34. North American T-6 Harvard (Texan in U.S. usage) training planes delivered to Canada during the period of U.S. neutrality were:

A. First flown to Bermuda, where they were transferred to the RCAF, before being flown to Canada
B. Flown to the U.S.—Canadian border, then pushed or pulled across before being flown to bases
C. Given civilian serial numbers, and transferred to Canadian civil airports as "pleasure craft"
D. Crated, and shipped across the border as "farm equipment"

35. Air Marshal Sir Arthur Harris, architect of RAF raids on Germany, got the idea for firebombing cities of the Reich:

A. While watching London in flames from the roof of the Air Ministry during the German blitz
B. From watching an army demonstration of flame-throwers
C. After reading Dante's *Inferno* for the third time
D. From a serious fire at his country estate

36. The Russian "air blockade" used first at Demyansk and Kholm in 1942-43 was intended to:

A. Stop all German fighters from reaching front-line Russian troops
B. Prohibit German supply convoys on the roads
C. Prevent German air transport from supplying pockets of surrounded German troops
D. Strike at German supply lines hundreds of miles behind the front lines

37. Soviet pilots disliked the LaGG-3 wooden fighter plane (the predecessor of the more successful La-5 and 7), and said the LaGG acronym stood for:

A. "Wooden wonder plane"
B. "Aircraft guaranteed not to work"
C. "The German secret weapon"
D. "Lacquered guaranteed coffin"

38. The *Zwilling* (twin) was:

A. A double gun mount in the wing of a FW-190 fighter
B. Two Ju-52's towing a large glider
C. Two He-111's joined together with a fifth engine between, used to tow enormous gliders
D. A pair of jet engines in one underwing pod on the *Arado 234* jet bomber

German, British, and American parachutes used by airborne troops each had unique characteristics. Which of the following had which trait (Note: one number has two correct answers):

39. ___ U.S.   A. Could not be steered by the risers
40. ___ British   B. The suspension lines opened before the chute
41. ___ German   canopy
                  C. The chute canopy opened first
                  D. Had a quick-release buckle which released the entire harness with a "smash" of the fist

42. These USAAF ground crew are rearming a:

A. P-38 Lightning
B. P-51 Mustang
C. P-47 Thunderbolt
D. P-39 Airacobra

Air Power Answer Key

1. C	10. D	19. D	28. C	37. D
2. D	11. B	20. D	29. D	38. C
3. B	12. E	21. A	30. A	39. C
4. D	13. B	22. C	31. C	40. B, D
5. E	14. C	23. B	32. B	41. A
6. A	15. B	24. E	33. B	42. C
7. D	16. A	25. C	34. B	
8. C	17. D	26. C	35. A	
9. B	18. C	27. D	36. C	

Naval Power

Sighted sub, sank same.

Donald F. Mason,
Radio message to U.S. Navy
Base, January 28, 1942

Unlike the war in the Pacific, the war in Europe was not one of hopping from island to island. Still, naval warfare was a major part of this theater of operations. The battle against the U-Boats, which sought to cut off England's vital supplies had to be won before the Allies could prevail elsewhere. Surface vessels, large and small, played roles on all fronts near large bodies of water. The amphibious landings in Africa, Italy, and France were the only way to get armies where they were needed.

1. The U.S. Navy captured the German submarine U-505 off the coast of Africa in early 1944. The sub was then:

A. Used by the U.S. Navy as the USS *Turbot* until it was lost in action
B. Lost while being towed, when the towing cable parted in mid-Atlantic
C. Briefly evaluated by the U.S. Navy, and towed to Chicago as a permanent museum exhibit
D. Turned over to the Free French Navy, and used by them until 1950, then scrapped

2. The *Schnorkel* device, used by U-Boats to supply air to crew and diesels while submerged, was a development of research begun in:

A. France
B. Norway
C. The USSR
D. The Netherlands

3. The *Bachstelze,* named for a German bird, was:

A. A powerless kite, driven by rotors, towed behind a U-Boat carrying an observer
B. A fake conning tower packed with explosives, towed behind a U-Boat to destroy any vessel which rammed it
C. A remote controlled missile launched by U-Boats to shoot down attacking Allied airplanes
D. An antiaircraft rocket towing a cable, used to entangle and destroy aircraft attacking U-Boat pens in France

Capital ships of the *Reichsmarine* were virtually all destroyed before the end of the war. Match each major German warship and its ultimate fate:

4. ___ *Tirpitz*	A. Scuttled off Uruguay, 1939
5. ___ *Bismarck*	B. Sunk in North Atlantic, 1941
6. ___ *Graf Spee*	C. Never completed, scuttled; salvaged by
7. ___ *Graf Zeppelin*	Russians
8. ___ *Adm. Scheer*	D. Bombed in Tromsofjord, 1944
9. ___ *Scharnhorst*	E. Bombed at Swinemunde, 1945
10. ___ *Luetzow*	F. Sunk off North Cape, 1943
(ex-*Deutschland*)	G. Scuttled at Gdynia, 1945
11. ___ *Gneisenau*	H. Bombed at Kiel, 1945

12. The Italian battleship *Roma* went to the bottom:

A. After being hit by a German air-to-surface missile
B. When torpedoed by an Italian submarine
C. When bombed by the RAF to prevent its use by the Germans
D. After an explosion of unknown origin amidships

13. The French battleship *Jean Bart* was:

A. Scuttled with the rest of the French fleet at Toulon on November 27, 1942
B. Put out of action by the USS *Massachusetts* during Operation Torch
C. Sunk by Royal Navy Swordfish torpedo planes at Mers-el-Kebir
D. At Martinique in the Caribbean when war broke out, and remained there until 1943

14. In 1941, the U.S. traded 50 World War I vintage destroyers to the British in exchange for bases in the Western Hemisphere. One of the destroyers, the USS *Buchanan,* was renamed HMS *Campbeltown;* its ultimate fate was:

A. Sunk as a blockship off Normandy in 1944
B. Packed with TNT, it was rammed into a German drydock at St. Nazaire, where it exploded
C. After ramming U-48, both ships sank together, with only 25 survivors
D. Donated to the Soviet Navy after being severely damaged while escorting a convoy to Murmansk

15. The Royal Navy Volunteer Reserve was dubbed the "Wavy Navy" because:

A. The officers waved rather than provide a proper salute
B. Inexperienced members took so long to get their "sea legs"
C. Their uniforms were usually terribly wrinkled
D. The rank insignia on officers' sleeves were "wavy" rather than straight

16. Kapitaen-Leutnant Guenther Prien:

A. Was the only survivor of the *Bismarck*
B. Sank HMS *Royal Oak* inside the Royal Navy base at Scapa Flow in 1939
C. Sank more merchant shipping than any other U-Boat captain in World War II
D. Was Admiral Doenitz's personal aide

17. Lothar Guenther Buchheim, author of the acclaimed novel *Das Boot* (The Boat) that was made into an award-winning movie, was, during the war:

A. A German war artist
B. Technical officer aboard a U-Boat
C. Captain of an E-Boat
D. A writer for the Propaganda Ministry

18. British wartime merchant marine shipping losses totaled:

A. 2½ million tons
B. 7½ million tons
C. 11½ million tons
D. 15½ million tons

19. Of 10,000 Norwegians killed in World War II, how many were merchant sailors:

A. 1,000
B. 3,000
C. 4,000
D. 6,000

20. After 1942, Allied naval superiority and long-range aircraft made the job of the U-Boats more difficult. How many U-Boats were sunk by Allied surface vessels:

A. 188
B. 246
C. 288
D. 342

21. Using the same numbers as above, tell how many U-Boats were destroyed by Allied aircraft (excluding bombing raids on submarine pens).

22. The "milch cow" submarines used to re-equip patrolling U-Boats at sea, and which were all rapidly sunk by the Allies, were designated:

A. Type VIII
B. Type XI
C. Type XIV
D. Type XVII

23. A general rule of thumb for submarine availability says that one-third of the boats are at their bases, one-third are en-route, and one-third are on station. On September 3, 1939, the *Kriegsmarine* had how many U-Boats:

A. 32
B. 57
C. 78
D. 101

24. The only U.S. battleships used in the European theater in 1944 were three older battleships which supported the amphibious landings in Normandy and Southern France. Which of these was *not* among them:

A. USS *Arkansas*
B. USS *Nevada*
C. USS *Florida*
D. USS *Texas*

A number of American destroyers became distinguished for a number of actions. Can you identify each "tin can"?

25. ___ USS *Pillsbury*	A.	First U.S. warship sunk in WWII
26. ___ USS *Reuben James*	B.	Rammed U-405, both ships then sank
27. ___ USS *Borie*	C.	Crew members boarded captured U-505

28. After the North African invasion, U.S. submarines in the Atlantic:

A. Continued to operate from their Scottish base
B. Moved to the Caribbean to protect oil tankers there
C. Were sent to the Pacific, leaving the Atlantic for the Allies
D. Were transferred to the Mediterranean

29. The S.S. *Athenia* was the first British ship sunk by a U-Boat during World War II, on September 3-4, 1939. The German government:

A. Claimed full responsibility
B. Claimed that 3 Royal Navy destroyers sank the *Athenia*
C. Claimed that passengers on the *Athenia* saw a whale rather than a torpedo wake in the water
D. Claimed that the *Athenia* struck an iceberg
E. B and C above

30. American shipbuilders mass-produced a great number of Liberty ships to replace shipping lost to submarines. The average speed of a Liberty ship was:

A. 7 knots
B. 11 knots
C. 15 knots
D. 19 knots

31. The "Channel Dash" was a great achievement for the *Kriegsmarine*, in which the *Scharnhorst, Gneisenau*, and *Prinz Eugen* successfully left their Channel ports and reached the open waters of the Atlantic. This dash took place on:

A. Sept. 15, 1941
B. Feb. 12, 1942
C. May 6, 1942
D. Nov. 11, 1942

32. One method of countering German air attacks on convoys by FW 200 Condor bombers was by mounting catapults on merchant ships to launch:

A. Supermarine Spitfires
B. Grumman Martlets
C. Fairey Swordfish
D. Hawker Hurricanes

33. The smallest American aircraft to sink a U-Boat was:

A. An armed T-6 of the Army Air Force
B. A Navy F4F Grumman Wildcat from an escort carrier
C. A civilian light plane of the Civil Air Patrol
D. A Vultee Vindicator from Air Training Command

34. These U.S. Coast Guardsmen are:

A. Lowering sonar gear to listen for submarines
B. Preparing minesweeping equipment
C. Adding auxiliary fuel tanks to their vessel
D. Loading a depth charge on its launcher

Naval Power Answer Key

1. C	8. H	15. D	22. C	29. E
2. D	9. F	16. B	23. B	30. B
3. A	10. E	17. A	24. C	31. B
4. D	11. G	18. C	25. C	32. D
5. B	12. A	19. C	26. A	33. C
6. A	13. B	20. C	27. B	34. D
7. C	14. B	21. B	28. C	

Commandos and Resistance

In war there is no second prize
for the runner-up.

Omar Bradley

Special forces such as the British Commandos and U.S. Army Rangers arose in World War II, as did the many anti-Nazi resistance groups in occupied Europe. Many of these groups had an impact far in excess of their numbers; others did not succeed. The bravery of both is undeniable.

1. The Germans, in their invasion of Holland, used which of the following deception techniques:

A. Germans dressed in Dutch uniforms to confuse the defenders
B. Dutch prisoners herded in front of German troops to prevent Dutch troops from firing on them
C. Both A and B

2. British "A" Force troops deceived Rommel before the El Alamein attack by:

A. Constructing a simulated fuel pipeline of gasoline cans
B. Covering tanks with "sunshields" to make them resemble trucks
C. Building a half-life-size railroad and terminal in the desert
D. Hiding artillery pieces in pits under trucks
E. All of the above

3. The Royal Army Commandos carried out their first large raid in March of 1941 on the Lofoten Islands in Norway. This raid resulted in:

A. The destruction of a Luftwaffe airfield used as a base to attack convoys, and the capture of a German general
B. The destruction of fish oil and fish meal factories, oil and gas tanks, and 11 small vessels, the recruitment of over 300 Norwegian volunteers for the Allied forces, and many Nazi and Quisling prisoners
C. The death or capture of most of the commandos when they were ambushed by the Germans, in a great setback for the commando movement
D. The destruction of a vital German radar base, and the return to England of many of its secret components

4. Orde Wingate, who had organized the Special Night Squads among Palestinian Jews in the 1930's, and who died in 1944 while commander of the Chindits in Burma, also:

A. Led Royal Army Commandos in raids on occupied France in 1942
B. Parachuted into France in 1941 in an unsuccessful attempt to organize resistance forces
C. Led "Gideon Force" to victory over the Italians in Ethiopia
D. Founded the British Airborne Divisions

5. General Robert Laycock, commando leader who tried to assassinate Rommel in Africa:

A. Was captured, then interrogated personally by Rommel. He later wrote *The Desert Fox* based on his experiences
B. Was unable to find the HQ and wandered for weeks with his commandos, striking targets of opportunity behind German lines
C. Was one of only two survivors of the failed attack, which struck when Rommel was elsewhere. Laycock and a sergeant spent two weeks in the desert with *The Wind in the Willows* as their only reading matter
D. Practically destroyed Rommel's HQ, wounded the Field Marshal, and then discovered a Luftwaffe airfield.

6. The raid on Dieppe, France, in August, 1942, by Canadian troops and British commandos was a costly operation, but provided Allied planners with important information for the planned invasion of the Continent. Of the 5,000 Canadians who participated, what percentage became casualties or prisoners?

A. 30%
B. 45%
C. 70%
D. 80%

7. General George Patton sent a force of 300 men toward the German prison camp at Hammelburg (where his son-in-law was held) to avoid a feared massacre. This force:

A. Was surrounded and destroyed by the Nazis before they reached the camp
B. Reached the camp, but were unable to free the prisoners and were forced to retreat
C. Liberated the prisoners, but were attacked and decimated on the return trip to American lines
D. Returned safely to Allied lines, but without Patton's son-in-law, who had been moved to another camp

8. The Denison smock was:

A. A roomy, camouflaged jacket worn by British paratroopers
B. A near-copy of the German paratrooper coverall, worn by British paratroopers
C. A leather jerkin worn over battle dress by most British soldiers in the field in cold weather
D. A coverall worn by Royal Tank Regiment troops in winter

9. U.S. Marines engaged in ground combat in Europe in small numbers. These Marines were:

A. Observers who landed with Royal Marine Commandos in early raids in Norway
B. Boat crew who came ashore at Normandy when their landing craft was sunk by enemy action
C. Crew of an antisubmarine PBT Catalina who ran out of fuel off France, swam ashore and joined the French Resistance
D. O.S.S. guerrillas who organized French resisters behind the German lines after D-Day

10. The first American ranger troops in World War II received special commando training at:

A. Achnacarry, Scotland
B. Camp Borden, Ontario
C. Brecon Beacons, Wales
D. Belfast, Northern Ireland

11. German parachute troops *(Fallschirmjaeger)* were mostly members of the:

A. Wehrmacht
B. Kriegsmarine
C. Waffen SS
D. Luftwaffe

12. The 1st Special Service Force, originally planned as a raiding force to operate in Norway, but which participated in combat in Italy and Southern France before being disbanded in late 1944, was made up of men of two nationalities. These were:

A. Australians and New Zealanders
B. British and South Africans
C. Americans and Canadians
D. British and Canadians

13. Soviet paratroopers were most often dropped in small numbers behind German lines to support partisan groups. Two exceptions to this practice occurred in January, 1942, when hundreds of Russian parachutists were dropped near:

A. Vyazma
B. Orel
C. Kharkov
D. Rostov

14. The favorite vehicle of the Long Range Desert Group in its early days was:

A. The British 3-ton 4-wheel-drive Austin K5 truck
B. The Daimler Mk. I Scout Car
C. A 30-cwt Chevrolet commercial truck, stripped down to reduce weight
D. The Canadian Dodge weapons carrier

15. The British commandos chose a forest green beret as their distinctive headgear, as did the U.S. Special Forces more recently. The first of these green berets were made by:

A. A distinguished London haberdasher
B. The official supplier to Canadian forces
C. A Scottish tam-o'-shanter maker
D. A Welsh hatter

16. General Draga Mihailovic was:

A. Leader of the Chetnik guerrillas in Yugoslavia
B. Josip Tito's second-in-command with the Yugoslav partisans
C. The puppet leader of German-dominated Croatia
D. The head of the Bulgarian government in exile in the USSR

Commandos and Resistance Answer Key

1. C	7. A	13. A
2. E	8. A	14. C
3. B	9. D	15. C
4. C	10. A	16. A
5. C	11. D	
6. C	12. C	

Acronyms,
Code Names and Slang

I have never met anybody who
wasn't against war. Even Hitler
and Mussolini were, according
to themselves.

David Low

Military and wartime life engenders its own language, one which is often incomprehensible not only to civilians, but also to members of other services. Acronyms such as radar (RAdio Detection And Ranging) were widespread. Code names to preserve the secrecy of upcoming operations, or devices, proliferated as never before. Service slang serves to deflate the pomposity of military life and people, and to express deep personal feelings about war, life, and death.

1. The German dive bomber Ju87 was known by its acronym, *Stuka,* which is short for:

A. Stumpfkabelflieger
B. Stufenkampfgeraet
C. Sturzflugkarosserie
D. Sturzkampfflugzeug
E. Stundenkartefliegerei

Both Axis and Allies used code names for upcoming operations in order to preserve secrecy. Match each code name with its objective:

2. ___ Market Garden A. RAF air raid on Friedrichshaven
3. ___ Bellicose   B. The aborted German invasion of Britain
4. ___ Sea Lion   C. The 1945 bombing of Dresden
5. ___ Plate Rack   D. The airborne landings in Arnhem and
6. ___ Chastise   nearby
7. ___ Hercules   E. The "Dambusters" raid
                       F. The planned German invasion of Malta

8. *Gestapo* was the acronym for the dreaded and hated German:

A. Gesicherte Stabspolizei
B. Gemeine Staffelpolizei
C. Gefaehrliche Starkerpolizei
D. Geheime Staatspolizei

GI's in Britain, as well as the local civilians, often had trouble understanding the expressions used by their fellow English-speakers. What do these English expressions mean?

9. ___ Knock up   A. An eraser
10. ___ Keep your pecker up B. Stay cheerful
11. ___ Wash up   C. Call on someone
12. ___ Rubber   D. Do the dishes

Army Air Forces slang was incomprehensible to many Americans, too, such as:

13. ___ Meat wagon A. Psychiatric discharge from the service
14. ___ Section 8   B. Routine or easy bombing mission
15. ___ Milk run   C. Ambulance

Different classes of U.S. Navy warships were named for different people, places, or things:

16. ___ Battleships   A. Major cities
17. ___ Battle cruisers   B. American war heroes
18. ___ Cruisers   C. States
19. ___ Destroyers   D. Fish
20. ___ Submarines   E. Territories

An enormous number of landing ships and landing craft were developed in World War II. While these were mostly employed in the Pacific, the landings in North Africa, Italy, and France required numbers of them, too. The acronyms for each of these types is a giveaway, so you will need to identify each type by its length in feet:

21. ___ LSD (Landing Ship, Dock)   A. 25 ft.
22. ___ LVT (Landing Vehicle, Tracked) B. 457 ft.
23. ___ LCI (Landing Craft, Infantry)   C. 50 ft.
24. ___ LSM (Landing Ship, Medium)   D. 158 ft.
25. ___ LCM (Landing Craft, Medium)   E. 200 ft.

26. A group of French resistance forces named themselves the *Maquis,* after:

A. The scrubby countryside of southwestern France
B. A marquis who was their early leader until captured, tortured, and killed by the Gestapo
C. The diamond-shaped insignia worn by them, copied from the divisional insignia of the French army in that area in 1940
D. The acronym for "fighting military men"

27. Lend-lease trucks, jeeps, and tanks delivered from the United States to the Soviet Union still bore their serial numbers with a prefix of "U.S.A." Soviet troops said the letters stood for:

A. "A gift from our American friends"
B. "Soviet-American friendship forever"
C. "Solidarity with American workers"
D. "Kill that son-of-a-bitch Adolf"

Secret and clandestine groups used acronyms, too. Match:

28. ___ OSS	A.	Communist guerrillas in France
29. ___ SOE	B.	A small group of British commandos and
30. ___ FFI		German Jews used in North Africa, nearly all
31. ___ FTP		were killed on their only mission
32. ___ SIG	C.	American spy and sabotage group
	D.	French resistance group loyal to General deGaulle
	E.	British spy and sabotage group

Acronyms, Code Names and Slang Answer Key

1. D	8. D	15. B	22. A	29. E
2. D	9. C	16. C	23. D	30. D
3. A	10. B	17. E	24. E	31. A
4. B	11. D	18. A	25. C	32. B
5. C	12. A	19. B	26. A	
6. E	13. C	20. D	27. D	
7. F	14. A	21. B	28. C	

D-Day

The first and great commandment is,
Don't let them scare you.

Elmer Davis

The Allied landing on Normandy on June 6, 1944, better known as D-Day, was the long-awaited opening of the second front against the Nazis. U.S., British, Canadian, and other troops arrived in Normandy by parachute, glider, or landing craft. Both Allied and Axis forces had made preparations for the attack.

1. From May 5 to June 2, five code names for the D-Day operations appeared in the London *Telegraph* crossword puzzle. Their appearance prompted MI5 to investigate but coincidence rather than espionage turned out to be the answer to this "puzzle." Which of the following words did *not* appear in the *Telegraph?*

A. Overlord
B. Mulberry
C. Juno
D. Omaha
E. Neptune
F. Utah

2. The German forces under Field Marshal Rommel had prepared many unpleasant surprises for the invading Allies, including many obstacles on the beaches and landing fields. *Rommelspargel* ("Rommel asparagus") consisted of:

A. Ditches in plowed fields to prevent glider landings.
B. Poles planted in open fields to deter glider landings.
C. Poles planted in the beaches to rip up landing craft.
D. Sharpened stakes intended to impale paratroopers.
E. A fast-growing ground cover to camouflage landing sites.
F. Tainted crops in Northern France to poison the invaders.

The British General Hobart designed a number of specialized armored vehicles to defeat beach defenses. These "Funnies" equipped the 79th Armored Division of the Royal Army, but the U.S. forces saw no need for them, and had a harder time crossing the beaches. Can you match the name of each "Funny" to its purpose?

3. ___ Crab
4. ___ Duplex Drive (DD)
5. ___ Bobbin
6. ___ Crocodile
7. ___ AVRE
8. ___ Ark

A. A device to unroll a canvas roadway over the sand.
B. An armored flame thrower.
C. Unfolding bridge girders on a tank, to allow others to pass over obstacles.
D. A tank made amphibious by addition of screw propellors and a raised canvas flotation screen.
E. A tank armed with the "Dustbin" spigot mortar (Petard), often also carrying fascines (bundles of brush used to fill in ditches)
F. A tank mounted with twirling chains in front intended to explode land mines

9. The 6th Airborne Division ("Red Devils") of the Royal Army used what instrument as a rallying signal upon landing?

A. A London bobby's whistle
B. An English hunting horn
C. An Irish pennywhistle
D. A snare drum

10. The U.S. airborne forces issued a device to individual paratroopers so they could recognize one another in the dark after dropping in Normandy. This device was:

A. A kazoo
B. A clicking metal "cricket" toy
C. A wooden duck call
D. A police whistle

11. The only Allied warship lost off the Normandy beachhead was the:

A. H.M.S. Warspite
B. U.S.S. Saginaw Bay
C. U.S.S. Corry
D. H.M.S. Botany

12. Theodore Roosevelt, Jr., son of the late President, begged his superiors for permission to land on Normandy. This was finally granted. General Roosevelt arrived on the beach and:

A. Was the first Allied general to be killed there
B. Was immediately wounded and sent to the hospital in France. He later distinguished himself fighting at the Siegfried Line
C. Was awarded the Medal of Honor for distinctive bravery in Normandy, given command of a Division, but died of a heart attack before assuming command
D. Was captured by the Germans and held prisoner until the liberation of his prison camp in Germany

13. The Luftwaffe attacked the landing beaches in the morning and evening of June 6, with, respectively:

A. 2 FW-190's and 6 Ju-88's
B. A squadron of FW-190's and 8 Me-109's
C. 3 squadrons of Me 262's and 4 FW-190's
D. 8 FW-190's and a mixed squadron of FW-190's and Me-109's

14. On the morning of the June 6th Allied invasion, Field Marshal Rommel, who had prepared so carefully, was:

A. At home in Stuttgart to celebrate Frau Rommel's birthday
B. In East Prussia, conferring with the Fuehrer
C. Asleep in his forward HQ in Le Havre
D. In Paris, meeting with Field Marshal von Runstedt

15. One of the devices tested for use in the invasion was the Great Panjan-drum, a rolling pair of wheels propelled by rockets and containing two tons of explosives. When demonstrated before a high-ranking contingent of ob-servers, the device ignominiously:

A. Headed out to sea, never to be seen again
B. Charged for the crowd, then headed to sea and exploded
C. Raced far inland, catapulted itself over a hill, and exploded in an aban-doned village
D. Failed to move at all, and had to be disarmed by a team of bomb defusing experts at great risk

16. An elite force of American troops had the objective of the cliffs at Pointe du Hoc, where intelligence indicated that German gun positions threatened Omaha Beach. After scaling these cliffs at great cost, these men found the gun mountings empty. This intrepid band named itself after its colonel, and was called:

A. Rudder's Rangers
B. Rogers' Rangers
C. Merrill's Marauders
D. Hogan's Heroes

17. The 4th Infantry Division of the U.S. Army suffered the following casualties on D-Day:

A. 12 killed, 185 other casualties
B. 52 killed, 388 other casualties
C. 152 killed, 208 other casualties
D. 575 killed, 2,100 other casualties

18. The 2nd SS Panzer Division *das Reich* was harrassed by both Allied air forces and French partisans on its way to Normandy from its base in Toulouse in southern France. The division finally arrived near the front in full force on:

A. June 15
B. June 22
C. June 27
D. June 30

and began actual combat on:

A. June 18
B. June 25
C. July 1
D. July 10

19. In an incident kept secret until quite recently, 749 American troops training for D-Day off Slapton Sands in England died in tragic circumstances, when:

A. They were shelled with live ammunition on the beach
B. Two of their LST's collided and quickly sank in deep water
C. An escorting medium bomber crashed into their ship, setting it afire
D. German E-boats torpedoed 3 LST's, sinking 2

20. The city of Caen, one of the early objectives of the invasion, proved a major obstacle to British and Canadian forces on the eastern edge of the battle front. The city finally fell on:

A. June 16
B. June 28
C. July 5
D. July 8

21. The "Falaise Pocket" was:

A. A surrounded group of German forces
B. An Allied salient cut off by a German counterattack
C. A haven for French Resistance forces south of the Allied lines
D. An unauthorized uniform alteration used by German occupying forces to stash loot in

22. The "bocage" was:

A. The famous cheese of the Southern region of Normandy, popular with both Germans and Allies
B. The name for the hedgerow countryside in Normandy
C. The nickname of the local Resistance forces
D. A French antitank rifle used by the Germans with little success

23. The farm country in Normandy was characterized by small rectangular fields bounded by dense hedgerows, or raised earthen walls topped by vegetation. These hedgerows provided the Nazis with strong, well-concealed defensive positions, which slowed down the Allied advance. The locally improvised Culin Hedgerow Device, named for its American sergeant inventor, was:

A. A gunsight and barrel attachment which permitted the user to shoot around corners, foiling ambushes
B. A powerful shaped explosive charge which blew large holes in hedgerows, permitting passage
C. A cutting fence, made of discarded German beach obstacles, which, welded on the front of tanks, allowed them to cut through hedgerows, rather than expose their undersides while climbing over
D. A high-pressure water hose which directed a stream of water onto the base of the hedgerow, washing it away so vehicles could pass through

24. As the landing area in Normandy had no natural harbors, the Allied planners devised a concrete artificial harbor designed to be towed across the English Channel and sunk in place off the beach. These Mulberry harbors:

A. Sank while being towed across the Channel and were lost
B. Did not fit in place as planned, and were abandoned
C. Were a success, but were severely damaged in storms a few weeks after D-Day
D. Worked so well that they are still in use today

25. Allied aircraft used in D-Day operations had conspicuous recognition markings consisting of:

A. Black and white stripes painted around fuselage and wings
B. Yellow cowlings, wing tips, and fuselage band
C. Solid white tail surfaces
D. Strings of amber lights on the wing leading edges

D-Day Answer Key

1. C	6. B	11. C	16. A	21. A
2. B	7. E	12. C	17. A	22. B
3. F	8. C	13. A	18. D, D	23. B
4. D	9. B	14. A	19. D	24. C
5. A	10. B	15. B	20. D	25. A

Army, Army Air Forces, and Navy
Slang

A "brass hat" is an officer of at least one rank higher than you whom you don't like and who doesn't like you.

Kenneth C. Royall

What do the following Army slang words signify?

1. ___ 5 x 5   A. A first sergeant
   (Five by five)   B. Medals and decorations
2. ___ Goldbrick   C. Intelligence section
3. ___ Fruit salad   D. A newly minted second lieutenant
4. ___ Topkick   E. A uniform stripe for years of service
5. ___ G-2   F. "I read you loud and clear"
6. ___ Shavetail   G. An easy, safe job, or one who seeks or obtains
7. ___ Hash mark   one

And these Navy terms?

8. ___ Pig boat   A. A Navy captain
9. ___ Tin can   B. One who has crossed the Equator
10. ___ Shellback   C. An aircraft carrier
11. ___ Four-striper   D. A destroyer
12. ___ Splinter Navy   E. A submarine
13. ___ Flattop   F. The Coast Guard Reserve

How about this Air Force terminology?

14. ___ Brolly   A. Abort a mission
15. ___ Scrub   B. Fighter escort aircraft
16. ___ Little Friend   C. Inflatable life vest
17. ___ Mae West   D. Low-level, strafing fighter sweep
18. ___ Rhubarb   E. Most dangerous position in bomber
19. ___ Coffin corner   formation
20. ___ Tail-end   F. Most dangerous position on a fighter mission
     Charlie   G. A parachute (from RAF usage)

And these Army vehicles?

21. ___ Peep   A. Late model Sherman tank with improved
22. ___ Deuce-and-a-   suspension, and more powerful 76mm. cannon
     half   B. 2½ ton amphibious truck
23. ___ Easy 8   C. Armored corps name for a jeep
24. ___ Duck   D. Popular, large 6-wheel Army truck

Army, Army Air Forces, and Navy Slang Answer Key

1. F	7. E	13. C	19. E
2. G	8. E	14. G	20. F
3. B	9. D	15. A	21. C
4. A	10. B	16. B	22. D
5. C	11. A	17. C	23. A
6. D	12. F	18. D	24. B

The Chow Line

An army marches on its stomach.

Napoleon Bonaparte

The U.S. Army developed a number of scientifically designed rations for field and combat troops, designating each with a letter or other symbol. Which ration was which:

1. ___ "C" ration
2. ___ "D" ration
3. ___ "K" ration
4. ___ "A" ration
5. ___ "B" ration
6. ___ "10-in-1" ration

A. Field ration using fresh milk, fruit, and vegetables
B. Variety package to supply a number of men in combat zone for one day
C. Field ration substituting canned milk, fruit, and vegetables for fresh where necessary
D. Balanced meal in cans for men cut off from normal food supply
E. Fortified chocolate bars for emergency use, discontinued after misuse
F. Compact, lightweight meals for combat and assault troops

For most servicemen, familiarity with military food bred contempt. Some of the slang terms reflect this dislike: (You must use one answer twice.)

7. ___ Armored cow
8. ___ Battery acid
9. ___ Collision mat (Navy usage)
10. ___ Dog food (or Kennel rations)
11. ___ Mud
12. ___ SOS

A. Coffee
B. Pancakes or waffles
C. Corned beef hash
D. Creamed chipped beef on toast
E. Canned condensed milk

13. The lemon drink mix in C-rations was:

A. The most popular beverage included
B. Often used successfully as hair rinse and floor cleaner
C. Discontinued early due to its unpopularity
D. B and C

14. The "K" ration was originally called the:

A. Iron ration
B. Armored ration
C. Paratrooper ration
D. Composition ration

15. The "10-in-1" ration evolved from the:

A. Jungle ration
B. Mountain ration
C. 5-in-1 ration
D. British "compo" or 14-in-1 ration
E. All of the above

16. The Air Forces Pocket Lunch, intended for use in single-seat fighter airplanes, consisted of:

A. An easy-opening can of fruit salad
B. A miniature sandwich on crackers
C. A mixture of confections
D. Fortified chocolate bars

17. The "Ration, Parachute, Emergency" weighed how much and contained how many calories?

A. 5 oz., 350 calories
B. 7½ oz., 500 calories
C. 11½ oz., 1,062 calories
D. 15 oz., 1,520 calories

The Chow Line Answer Key

1. D	7. E	13. D
2. E	8. A	14. C
3. F	9. B	15. E
4. A	10. C	16. C
5. C	11. A	17. C
6. B	12. D	

Landmines
A Potpourri of Questions to Blow Your Mind

Shoot first and inquire afterwards,
and if you make mistakes,
I will protect you.

Hermann Goering

Some of these questions do not fit neatly into any of the preceding categories; the answers to others would be self-evident if the questions were included in those chapters. Here goes!

1. On August 31, 1939, the Germans staged an incident which they used to provoke their attack on Poland. It consisted of:

A. A phony attack, supposedly by the Polish Army, on a Silesian border village in Germany
B. A bombing raid on an East Prussian town by the Luftwaffe posing as the Polish Air Force
C. Naval shelling of the city of Kolberg, purportedly by the Polish Navy
D. Artillery and mortar shelling of a Pomeranian town, by the Wehrmacht, but attributed to the Poles

2. When a top-secret radar set aboard a Luftwaffe night fighter plane wound up in Switzerland, the Swiss destroyed it in exchange for:

A. $5 million in gold
B. The sale of 12 Messerschmitt 109G aircraft
C. A German promise to end overflights by the Luftwaffe
D. 25 new Tiger tanks

3. The Belgian fort of Eben Emael fell to the Germans in May, 1940:

A. Under constant shelling by German 42cm howitzers
B. To 55 paratroopers who landed on the fortress roof in gliders
C. Due to sabotage by disloyal Belgian troopers in the fort's garrison
D. After costly frontal assaults by the Wehrmacht

4. General Sikorski, former Prime Minister of Poland, and commander of the Polish Army in exile, died:

A. By an assassin's bullet while reviewing Polish troops in North Africa
B. In the battle for Monte Cassino, while leading his troops there
C. When his airplane crashed into the Mediterranean upon takeoff from Gibraltar
D. In the final phase of the 1944 Warsaw Uprising

5. The Mannerheim Line was:

A. A telephone transmission line strung by front-line German communications troops in Poland in 1939
B. The official party propaganda line of the Free Germany Committee, the exiled German Communists in Moscow
C. The Finnish defense line against the Soviet attack in 1940
D. The Austrian steamship line, appropriated by the Nazis in 1939

6. The British or Commonwealth officer who destroyed the most Axis aircraft was:

A. S/Ldr George ("Buzz" or "Screwball") Beurling, RCAF
B. Lt. Col. "Paddy" Mayne, SAS
C. Grp/Capt. Peter Townsend, RAF
D. Grp/Capt. C.R. "Killer" Caldwell, RAAF

7. M3 was the U.S. Army designation for:

A. The "Grease Gun" .45 cal. submachine gun
B. The "Stuart" light tank
C. The "Grant-Lee" medium tank
D. A half-track armored personnel carrier
E. All of the above
F. A and C above only

Sherman and other Allied tank chassis were converted to self-propelled guns or armored personnel carriers. Match the following names to their vehicles:

8. ___ Sexton   A. 105mm. howitzer on Sherman chassis
9. ___ Priest   B. A tank or SP vehicle with armament removed,
10. ___ Archer   used as personnel carrier
11. ___ Kangaroo   C. 25-pdr mounted on Valentine chassis
12. ___ Bishop   D. 25-pdr on Ram (Canadian Sherman) chassis
                       E. 17-pdr antitank gun on Valentine chassis

13. "Anzio Annie" was:

A. Mussolini's mistress in 1942
B. A German railway artillery piece which shelled the Anzio beachhead
C. The Italian propaganda counterpart to "Tokyo Rose" and "Axis Sally"
D. A popular dancer, prostitute, and spy in Italy, working for British intelligence in 1941

14. The Red Army news photographer Tyomin "scooped" his colleagues by taking the first photo of the Red flag over the Reichstag from an airplane. He then flew to Moscow in Marshal Zhukov's plane, and back to Berlin with the Red Army newspaper victory edition with his photo just as his fellow press members arrived. In his absence, Zhukov had:

A. Awarded him the Order of the Red Star
B. Ordered him shot for stealing the plane
C. Given Tyomin up for lost, along with the aircraft
D. Ordered the Red Army to withdraw from the Reichstag area under heavy fire

15. The nickname "Black Death" was bestowed by the Nazi forces on:

A. The Latvian Waffen SS division, which fought on to the very end in Berlin
B. The Royal Marine Commandos of the Royal Navy
C. The Soviet Black Sea Marines
D. U.S. Coast Guard antisubmarine forces

16. The Katyn forest, west of Smolensk in the USSR, is best known for:

A. Harboring large numbers of Soviet partisans, who fought off all Nazi attempts to eliminate them
B. A major German breakthrough in 1941, in which German Panzers emerged from the forest unexpectedly, scoring great success
C. The massacre in 1940 of over 4,000 Polish officers and men captured by the Russians in 1939
D. Being the center of a major German pincer movement, which cut off hundreds of thousands of Russians who were made prisoners

17. The Russian advance on Berlin was massive. The Soviet forces included:

A. 500,000 men and 2,100 tanks
B. 1 million men and 3,200 tanks
C. 2 million men and 6,300 tanks
D. 3½ million men and 8,000 tanks

18. The German 250th Division (Blue Division, or *Division Azul*) was made up of Spanish Fascist "volunteers." They fought near Leningrad from late 1941 to early 1944, but were disbanded when:

A. Casualties had become so high that the division practically ceased to exist as a functional unit
B. The division retreated in great disorder when beset by massed Russian troops and tanks in a major counterattack
C. Lack of equipment and language difficulties between Germans and Spaniards caused the division to fail in an important German thrust
D. England, protesting Spain's lack of neutrality, embargoed food and fuel shipments to Spain

19. An American division, whether fighting or not, was said to require _____ tons of supplies daily:

A. 175
B. 325
C. 650
D. 950

20. The neutral Swedes were in an awkward position during World War II. They traded with both the Germans and the Allies, with iron ore and steel products important among their exports. How much iron ore did Sweden export to Germany in 1943:

A. 1 million tons, 5% of German needs
B. 4 million tons, 20% of German needs
C. 6 million tons, 38% of German needs
D. 10 million tons, 28% of German needs

21. The Swedish government refused to supply German troops in Narvik, but did allow the Germans to:

A. Fly bombers over Sweden en route to Norway
B. Transport a total of 2 million German troops to and from Norway between July, 1940, and August 1943
C. Buy several thousand Bofors anti-aircraft guns
D. Use Swedish naval bases for supply and repairs until May, 1943

22. On October 1 and 2, 1943, the Nazis went to round up the Jews of Denmark for deportation and extermination. The Danish underground knew of these plans, and hid or smuggled out:

A. 2,000 of 3,500 Jews
B. 5,000 of 6,000 Jews
C. 7,500 of 8,000 Jews
D. 9,000 of 11,000 Jews

23. The U.S. Army Veterinary Service, a branch of the Medical Services, had several important missions. What is the correct order of their importance?

A. ___ Conduct veterinary laboratory services concerned with food and various types of research
B. ___ Inspect food for the military, including processing and sanitation of food processors
C. ___ Provide comprehensive animal service
D. ___ Coordinate reestablishment of veterinary services, livestock and production of biologicals in war-torn lands

24. Before U.S.-trained war dogs arrived in Europe after the Channel crossing in June, 1944, the Army and Army Air Forces obtained the dogs they used in Britain from:

A. The British Ministry of Aircraft Production
B. The Royal Army Medical Corps
C. The Humane Society of Great Britain
D. The Royal Navy Volunteer Reserve

Women served in the armed forces and auxiliary services of most major combatants. Identify the following from their acronyms:

25. ___ WAAC
26. ___ WAVES
27. ___ WASPS
28. ___ SPARS

A. Women pilots
B. Women in the U.S. Army
C. Women in the U.S. Navy
D. Women in the U.S. Coast Guard

Some of the British, Commonwealth and German women's services follow and also need to be matched up:

29. ___ ATA
30. ___ WAAS
     (Waasies)
31. ___ WRNS
     (Wrens)
32. ___ RAD

A. Labor service for German women
B. Women in the British Royal Navy
C. Women aircraft ferry pilots
D. South African women's services

33. Cold injury, such as frostbite and trench foot, is a debilitating condition suffered most often by infantry troops in cold, wet climates. The U.S. Army experienced many cases of trench foot, primarily in the winter of 1944-45. How many cases of cold injury were there in the Army in World War II, and how many of these were in early 1945?

A. 30,000 cases, 25,000 in 1945
B. 50,000 cases, 30,000 in 1945
C. 70,000 cases, 35,000 in 1945
D. 90,000 cases, 40,000 in 1945

34. Brazil declared war on Germany in 1942, and Brazilian air and naval forces participated in the battle against the U-Boats. What did the Brazilian army contribute to the war effort?

A. Brazilian troops trained for combat with the Americans, but only arrived in Europe at the end of hostilities
B. A Brazilian Expeditionary Force fought in Italy from the campaign near Naples to the end of the war
C. Brazilian forces furnished garrison troops in the Caribbean and West Africa
D. A Brazilian Expeditionary Force landed in Normandy, and fought all the way to Germany

American Lend-Lease shipments of military medical supplies went to many countries. The primary recipients, and amounts received were:

35. ___ Soviet Union   A. $50 million
36. ___ French Africa   B. $38 million
37. ___ United Kingdom and dominions   C. $5 million

38. In the winter of 1944, 23 dog sled teams were sent to France to help evacuate American wounded through the deep snow. These dogs:

A. Were a great success, but demand for them always exceeded supply
B. Were not used for their original purpose, as the snow melted as soon as the dogs arrived
C. Were eaten by the troops who were surrounded by Germans
D. Were eaten by French civilians in the area, who were cut off from their usual food supply

39. On October 14, 1943, 291 8th Air Force B-17's left England for Schweinfurt to bomb the ball-bearing factories there. How many B-17's did not return?

A. 25
B. 38
C. 50
D. 60

40. The Warsaw Uprising (by the Polish Home Army, months after the liquidation of the Warsaw Jewish ghetto) went on from:

A. July 1 to September 1, 1944
B. August 1 to October 9, 1944
C. September 2 to October 25, 1944
D. September 25 to October 9, 1944

41. The Soviet Army, which was only across the river from Warsaw, then took the city on:

A. September 24, 1944
B. October 27, 1944
C. December 23, 1944
D. January 17, 1945

Russian vocabulary quiz. What do these Russian words mean:

42. ___ Katyusha   A. The muddy season
43. ___ Stavka   B. Deliberate ramming of enemy aircraft with
44. ___ Taran   one's own fighter
45. ___ Shtormovik C. Red Army General Staff
46. ___ Rasputitsa D. An armored ground attack airplane
                    E. A bombardment rocket

47. The Soviet Army autopsy report on the body of Adolf Hitler stated that:

A. Hitler shot himself
B. Hitler poisoned, rather than shot, himself
C. Hitler had only one testicle
D. Someone tested the poison on Hitler's favorite dog, Blondi
E. A and C above
F. B, C, and D above

Landmine Answer Key

1. A	11. B	21. B	31. B	41. D
2. B	12. C	22. C	32. A	42. E
3. B	13. B	23. B, C, A, D	33. D	43. C
4. C	14. B	24. A	34. B	44. B
5. C	15. C	25. B	35. B	45. D
6. B	16. C	26. C	36. C	46. A
7. E	17. C	27. A	37. A	47. F
8. D	18. D	28. D	38. B	
9. A	19. C	29. C	39. D	
10. E	20. D	30. D	40. B	

FURTHER READING

There are too many books about World War II to list all of them here.

A number of excellent pictorial works exist. There are two useful series, each containing numerous color and black-and-white illustrations of aircraft, armored vehicles, uniforms and insignia: the Arco-Aircam series on individual aircraft and air forces; and the Osprey series (from Britain) entitled "Men-at-Arms" (for uniforms, etc.) and "Vanguard" (for armored vehicles and campaigns). Squadron/Signal publications issues a number of illustrated books about tanks and warplanes. The Profile series from England, long out of print, but now becoming available again, is a series of many small booklets covering armor and aircraft. Local bookstores or hobby shops may stock many of these.

Consult your local library about the U.S. government depository library nearest you for the many publications by the Department of Defense and its predecessor agencies. *The U.S. Army in World War II* is a series of volumes covering World War II in infinite detail.

Among the best histories and memoirs about World War II in Africa and Europe is Dwight Eisenhower's classic *Crusade in Europe* (New York: Doubleday, 1948), a top-level view of Allied strategy and operations from North Africa to D-Day. Field Marshal Bernard Law Montgomery's histories include 3 volumes, paramount among them *El Alamein to the River Sangro* (London: Hutchinson, 1948). A German view of several fronts is Fridolin von Senger and Etterlin's *Neither Fear Nor Hope* (New York: Dutton, 1964), by the Axis commander at Monte Cassino and elsewhere in Italy. The Eastern Front is well-covered by Paul Carell (Paul Karl Schmidt) in *Hitler Moves East, 1941-43* (Boston: Little, Brown, 1965) and *Scorched Earth* (Boston: Little, Brown, 1970). Schmidt has also written *Foxes of the Desert* (London: McDonald, 1960), a history of the *Africa Korps*. Readers interested in naval war against U-Boats and German surface raiders may read Walter Karig's *Battle Reports, Volume 2: The Atlantic War* (New York: Farrar & Rinehart, 1945). Anthony Verrier's *The Bomber Offensive* (New York: Macmillan, 1969) is a detailed history of the RAF and USAAF air actions against Germany.

ORDER NOW...
WORLD WAR II TRIVIA QUIZ BOOK, VOLUME 2, THE PACIFIC

"Erhard Konerding's TRIVIA QUIZ BOOK, VOLUME 2: THE PACIFIC is as:

Felicitous as MacArthur's Hollandia strategy

Unbeatable as the second wave at Tarawa

Necessary as Atabrine to understanding the Pacific War."

— *William Manchester*

To reserve a copy of WORLD WAR II TRIVIA QUIZ BOOK Volume 2 **return the form below, along with your check in the correct amount, to:**

Southfarm Press, P.O. Box 1296, Middletown, CT 06457

_____ Number of copies WORLD WAR II TRIVIA QUIZ BOOK Volume 2: The Pacific

Name _____

Address _____

City _____ State _____ ZIP _____

Payment enclosed: $_____ .

Note: Price per book is $ 6.95 (U.S. dollars) PLUS $1.00 postage and handling

MONEY-BACK GUARANTEE.
Please allow 4 to 6 weeks for delivery.

available upon request

COMING FEBRUARY 1, 1986

Vietnam *War*
FACTS QUIZ

by Erhard Konerding

**To reserve a copy
return the form below**

- -

_____. Number of copies

Name _____

Address _____

City _____ State _____ ZIP _____

Payment enclosed: $_____ .

Note: Price per book is $ 6.95 (U.S. dollars) PLUS $1.00 postage and handling

Southfarm Press, P.O. Box 1296, Middletown, CT 06457

MONEY-BACK GUARANTEE.
Please allow 4 to 6 weeks for delivery.